Tell Tales

Snow White

THE BROTHERS GRIMM

Retold by Michael Rosen

Illustration: Agustí Asensio

Firefly

Once long ago in the middle of winter, when the snow was falling, a Queen sat doing her embroidery on a piece of cloth that was stretched over a black wooden frame. As she looked up at the snow, she pricked her finger with the needle and three drops of blood fell on to the snow.

'If only I had a child who was as white as snow, as red as blood and as black as this wood,' she said to herself.

A little while later, she gave birth to a girl with black hair, red lips and white skin and they called her Snow White. But when she was born the Queen died and the King looked for someone else to marry.

The woman he married was beautiful. She had a magic mirror and kept looking at herself and saying,

'Mirror, mirror, on the wall
Who's the most beautiful of us all?'
The mirror said,
'You, oh Queen, you are.'

But as Snow White grew older she became more and more beautiful until one day, when the Queen spoke to the mirror it said:

'You, oh Queen, are beautiful, it's true
but Snow White is more beautiful than
    you.'

The Queen was furious. Every time she saw Snow White after that, she hated her. One day she sent for a huntsman and said, 'Get that child out of my sight; take her into the forest and kill her. Bring me her liver and lungs to prove that you've done it.'

The huntsman took Snow White into the forest but when he was about to kill her, Snow White called out.

'Let me live, huntsman, I'll run off through the woods and never come home again.'

The huntsman took pity and thought, the wild beasts will soon eat her anyway, so he said,

'Run away child.'

He killed a wild deer and took its liver and lungs back to the Queen. The cook stewed them up and the Queen ate them thinking she was eating Snow White's liver and lungs.

Snow White ran, running over sharp stones and through brambles. Just before night, she saw a little house and went in to rest. Inside everything was very clean and neat, but very, very small. On the table there were seven little plates and seven little cups. By the wall there were seven little beds. Snow White was very hungry and thirsty, so she ate a bit of bread from each plate and drank a sip from each cup. Then when she was tired, she lay down on one of the beds and fell asleep.

When it was quite dark, the owners of the little house came home. They were seven dwarfs who went off to the mountains everyday to dig for silver.

'Who's been sitting in my chair?' said one.

'Who's been eating off my plate?' said another.

'Who's been eating my bread?' said the third.

'Who's been eating my carrots?' said the fourth.

'Who's been using my fork?' said the fifth.

'Who's been using my knife?' said the sixth.

'Who's sleeping in my bed?' said the seventh.

'What's your name?' said the dwarfs.
'Snow White.'
'How did you get here?'
Snow White told them what had happened and they told her how they went off each day to the mountains to look for silver.
'You can stay here, Snow White,' they said, 'but watch out for the Queen. She'll soon find out you're here. Don't let anyone in.'

At the palace the Queen stood in front of
the mirror.

'Mirror, mirror on the wall, who is the
most beautiful of us all?' and the mirror
said, 'You, oh Queen are beautiful, it's true
but Snow White is more beautiful
than you.
She has found a place to stay,
with seven dwarfs far away.'

When she heard the mirror say that, she
shook with rage and shouted,
    'Snow White must die!'
    Then she went to a secret room and
made a very poisonous apple. It looked
so nice on the outside, with red cheeks,
that anyone who saw it would want it.
But anyone who ate even the tiniest bit of
it would die. When it was ready she
dressed up as an old woman and made
her way across seven mountains to the
house of the seven dwarfs.

She knocked and Snow White came to the window.

'I can't let anyone in,' she said, 'the seven dwarfs won't let me.'

'It doesn't matter,' said the old woman, 'I only want to get rid of these apples. Here, I'll give you one as a present.'

'No,' said Snow White, 'I'm not allowed to take anything.'

'Are you afraid of poison?' said the old woman.

'Look, I'm cutting it in half. You eat the red bit and I'll eat the green bit.'

But the apple had been made so cleverly, that only the red cheek was poisoned. Snow White longed to eat the lovely apple and when she saw the old woman take a bite out of it, she couldn't stop herself. She held out her hand, and took the poisonous half. But the moment she took a bite out of it, she fell to the floor, dead.

At work, high in the mountains, the seven dwarfs knew that something was wrong and hurried home. They found Snow White lying on the floor. No breath came out of her mouth. They lifted her up, combed her hair, washed her in water and wine, but nothing helped. She was dead.

So the seven dwarfs sat down beside her
and cried over her for a day and a night.
They got ready to bury her but she looked
fresh and alive.

'We can't put her in the earth,' they said,
so they made her a glass coffin so that she
could be seen from all sides. They put the
coffin on a hill top and one of them always
stayed there to guard it. And the birds
came to weep for Snow White.

One day, a prince came to the hill and he
saw Snow White inside.

'Let me have the coffin,' he said, 'I'll pay
you as much as you like for it.'

'We wouldn't part with it for all the
money in the world,' said the dwarfs.

'Then give it to me,' said the prince. 'I
would like to look on this Snow White
every day for the rest of my life.'

The dwarfs took pity on him and gave him the coffin. The prince's servants hoisted it up on their shoulders but as they were carrying it away one of them tripped. The bump shook the poisoned bit of apple out of Snow White's throat and she woke up. She opened her eyes, lifted the coffin lid and said,

'Oh, where am I?'

'With me,' said the prince. 'Will you come to my father's castle and be my wife?'

Snow White fell in love with the prince and went with him and arrangements were made for a wonderful feast.

The wicked Queen was one of the people invited to the wedding. She put on her fine clothes and went to the mirror and said,

    'Mirror, mirror on the wall,
    Who is the most beautiful of us all?'
and the mirror said,

    'Oh Queen, you are beautiful, it's true,
    but Snow White is more beautiful
      than you.'

In a great rage, she smashed the mirror against the wall. At first she didn't want to go to the wedding but in the end she couldn't help but go and see. The moment she arrived, she recognized Snow White, but the Queen was so terrified she just stood there and couldn't move. Two iron slippers had been made red-hot in the fire and the Queen was forced to step into them and dance until she fell to the floor dead.